COLOUR-BY -NUMBERS

MASTER PIECES

UNWIND AND RELEASE YOUR CREATIVITY BY BRINGING ART TO LIFE

This edition published by Parragon Books Ltd in 2017

Parragon Books Ltd
Chartist House
15–17 Trim Street
Bath BA1 1HA, UK
www.parragon.com

ISBN 978-1-4748-3832-0
Printed in China

COLOUR-BY-NUMBERS
MASTER PIECES

UNWIND AND RELEASE YOUR CREATIVITY BY BRINGING ART TO LIFE

PaRragon

Bath · New York · Cologne · Melbourne · Delhi
Hong Kong · Shenzhen · Singapore

HOW TO USE THIS BOOK

Match the numbers with the colours to recreate some genuine works of art! Look at the numbers in the artwork and pair these up with the numbers in the colour bar at the bottom of the image – this bar will guide you as to which colours to use in the different parts of the picture.

The images can be coloured in with either colouring pencils or felt-tip pens. If you don't have a colouring pencil or pen that is identical to the shade in the colouring bar then just pick a tone that is as close as possible. As long as the colour is similar, it will not affect the overall look of the masterpiece so just work with what you have available. If a part of the image doesn't have a number, leave it uncoloured.

The pictures in this book are arranged with all the portrait-shaped images first and are then followed by all the landscape-shaped images, so just turn the book around to start the landscape pictures. These colour-by-numbers masterpieces are relaxing to complete and should take anything from 30 minutes to up to an hour to complete, but there is no restriction on how long you can spend on these. These colour-by-numbers images will allow you to explore your creativity, particularly if you are not confident at drawing or sketching, so even a novice can recreate these beautiful works of art and unleash their imagination.

Once you've coloured in all of the images, you could remove each picture and frame the resulting image for a truly unique piece of art. The perforations along each page allow you to tear out any masterpiece, so you could give these to friends or display them around your own home.

The back pages of this book provides a small preview of each completed image, so be careful not to look at these in advance if you want to avoid a spoiler of the final results!

1 2 3 4 5 6 7 8 9 A B C D E F G H I

1 2 3 4 5 6 7 8 9 A B C D E F G H I J K L

1 2 3 4 5 6 7 8 9 A B C D E F G H I

1 2 3 4 5 6 7 8 9 A B C D E

5. *Self Portrait* by Van Gogh

7. *The Scream* by Munch

9. *The Kiss* by Klimt

11. *Ophelia* by Millais

13. *The Sistine Madonna* by Raphael

15. *Liberty Leading the People* by Delacroix

17. *The Balcony* by Manet

19. *Parham's Mill* by Constable

21. *Mäda Primavesi* by Klimt

23. *Bal du Moulin de la Galette* by Renoir

25. *Whistlejacket* by Stubbs

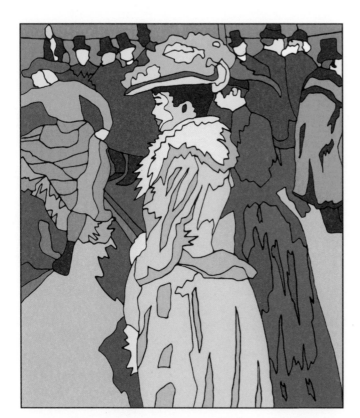

27. *At The Moulin Rouge, The Dance* by Lautrec

29. *Portrait of Henry VIII* by Holbein the Younger

31. *Portrait of Madame X* by Singer Sargent

33. *Beata Beatrix* by Rossetti

35. *Dancer with a Bouquet of Flowers* by Degas

37. *Portrait of Irene d'Anvers* by Renoir

39. *Portrait of a Man in a Red Turban* by Van Eyck

41. *The Laughing Cavalier* by Hals

43. *Portrait of a Young Woman* by Botticelli

45. *Self Portrait* by Rembrandt

47. *Seated Woman with Bent Knee* by Schiele

49. *The Arnolfini Portrait* by Van Eyck

51. *Sunflowers* by Van Gogh

53. *Mona Lisa* by Da Vinci

55. *Girl with a Pearl Earring* by Vermeer

57. *American Gothic* by Wood

59. *The Great Wave* by Hokusai

61. *The Starry Night* by Van Gogh

63. **Whistler's Mother** by Whistler

65. *La Maja Vestida* by Goya

67.*Parau Api* by Gauguin

69. *Traumgarten* by Rousseau

71. *Leda and the Swan* by Michelangelo

73. *Water Lilies* by Monet

75. *Venus and Adonis* by Rubens

77. *The Rokeby Venus* by Velázquez

79. *Bathers at Asnières* by Seurat

81. *Ivy Bridge* by Turner

83. *The Card Players* by Cézanne

85. *In the Conservatory* by Manet